Kittys
BIG
Ideas

Have you read all of these great books about Kitty?

I don't want to!
I can't find it!
It's not fair!
But you promised!
Why not?
I know!
I'm scared!
I wish!
Why me?
I'm bored!
It's not my fault!
So what!

Kitty's BIG Ideas

Bel Mooney

Illustrated by Margaret Chamberlain

EGMONT

First published in Great Britain 2002
by Egmont Books Limited,
239 Kensington High Street, London, W8 6SA

Original Kitty and Friends books © 1985, 1988,
1989, 1990, 1991, 1994, 1995, 1996, 1997,
1999, 2002 Bel Mooney
Illustrations © 1985, 1988, 1989, 1990,
1991, 1994, 1995, 1996, 1997, 1999,
2002 Margaret Chamberlain
Text adaption and compilation by Emily Gale

ISBN 1 4052 0198 3

10 9 8 7 6 5 4 3 2 1

A CIP catalogue record for this title
is available from the British Library

Printed in Hong Kong

HANDS OFF!!

This book belongs to:

....

CONTENTS

A letter from **Kitty**

Hi **Everyone!**

We all have our grumbles, don't we? Mum grumbles about messy bedrooms. Dad grumbles about cheeky daughters! My friend Rosie grumbles about being the youngest, and my brother Daniel grumbles when I'm right instead of him! And what I grumble about most of all is <u>BEING BORED.</u>

But it's no good just waiting for something exciting to happen. It's better to make your own fun — and that's the reason for this book. I've filled it with all sorts of good ideas for things to make you UN-bored, and there are bits for you to fill in, too — well I couldn't write the whole book by myself!

Love,

Kitty xxx

p.s. I hope you like the Kitty badge!

Chapter 1

All about **Kitty**
(and her friends)

How well do you think you know Kitty?
Do you know what her favourite toy is,
or what things she dislikes the most?
Can you remember the name of her
baby brother, or her snooty cousin?
This chapter tells you all about Kitty,
her family and her friends. There's
even a page for you to fill out.

Name: *Kitty* (a.k.a. Kit-Kat)

Likes: *bike riding, drawing, reading*

Dislikes: *tidying her bedroom, bossy GUs*

Favourite thing: *Mr Tubs*

Worst habit:
not doing her homework, ← YUK!
not eating her vegetables,
losing things

Most likely to say:
'I'm bored! Why not?
It's not my fault! So what!
I can't find it! I don't
want to! I know! I'm scared!
Why me? But you promised!
It's not fair! I wish!'

Least likely to say:
'I wish I had more
homework.'

Favourite moment:
being the first person
to make her baby
brother smile.

Name: *Ann*

Relation to Kitty: *mum*

Likes: *relaxing in a bubble bath*

Dislikes: *disorganisation* ← Mum loves long words

Favourite thing: *Daniel, Kitty and Tom!*

Worst habit:
getting cross in the morning when everyone's running late

Most likely to say:
'Kitty, you're the naughtiest child in England!'

Least likely to say:
'Of course you don't have to tidy your room, Kit-Kat.'

Favourite Kitty moment:
Kitty pretending to be 'Mum' so that the real Mum could have some time to herself.

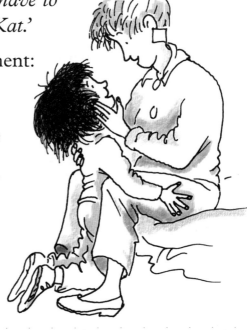

Name: *Ben*

Relation to Kitty: *dad*

Likes: *surprises, fish 'n' chips*

Dislikes: *impertinence*

Favourite thing: *Daniel, Kitty and Tom!*

(and Mum, of course)

Worst habit: *snoring*

Most likely to say:
'Who wants to go on an adventure?'

Least likely to say:
'Leave your vegetables if you don't like them, Kitty.'

VEGGY-TROUBLES!!

Favourite Kitty moment:
the surprise dinner she arranged in the garden for her mum and dad's anniversary.

Name: *William*

Relation to Kitty:
friend and next-door neighbour

Likes: *animals, gardening*

Dislikes: *being on stage*

Favourite thing: *bicycle*

Worst habit: *always ~~winning~~* losing *at games*

Most likely to say: *'I've won again!'*

Least likely to say:
'Girls are better than boys.' ← As if!!

Favourite Kitty moment:
During the Nativity Play when William was playing Joseph, Kitty made him laugh so that he would forget about being nervous – it worked!

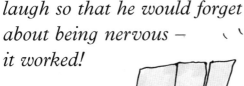

Name: *Rosie*

Relation to Kitty:
friend and classmate

Likes: *her grandma's
Jamaican cooking,
sports*

Dislikes: *silly boys*

Favourite thing:
sports bag

Worst habit:
occasional bad moods

Most likely to say:
'*Let's have a race!*'

Rosie is the
fastest girl in
the class.

Least likely to say:
'*Let's play Sleeping Lions.*'

Favourite Kitty moment:
*On Rosie's first day at school, Kitty was
chosen to show her round and they've been
great friends ever since.*

Name: *Anita*

Relation to Kitty: *friend and classmate*

Likes: *hanging out with Kitty*

Dislikes: *bullies*

Favourite thing: *a beautiful sari from India*

Worst habit: *being too shy*

Most likely to say:
'Please!' and 'Thank you!' ←

Anita is much more polite than me!

Least likely to say:
'Let's have a shouting competition!'

Favourite Kitty moment:
Kitty stood up to the people who were bullying Anita on the way home from school – Anita thought that was the bravest thing ever.

Name: *Melissa*

Relation to Kitty: *cousin*

Likes: *putting on make-up, playing with dolls, skipping*

Dislikes: *insects, getting dirty*

Favourite thing: *pink dress with bow* ← Eurgh!

Worst habit: *twiddling hair, being snooty*

Most likely to say:
'It's nice to look pretty for others – and not be a big scruff-bag like Kitty!'

Least likely to say:
'Let's climb that enormous tree!' ↖ Hey!

Favourite Kitty moment:
the time Kitty stood up for Melissa when some boys were teasing her in William's garden.

If you've read Kitty's 11th book, *It's not my fault!*, you'll know that her snooty cousin Melissa isn't snooty any more! She calls herself Mel now and she's much more fun than she used to be. Here's *new* Mel's profile, and later on Kitty will tell you all about the *old* Mel.

Name: *Mel*

Relation to Kitty: *cousin*

Likes: *parties, hanging out with friends, clothes*

Dislikes: *the way she used to be!*

Favourite thing: *her oldest doll*

Worst habit: *being bossy*

Most likely to say: *'Just call me Mel!'*

Least likely to say: *'I'm the Beauty and you're the Beast, Kitty!'*

Favourite Kitty moment: *the look on Kitty's face when she saw Mel's new haircut!*

much better!

Name: *Daniel*

Relation to Kitty: *big brother*

Likes: *cricket, TV*

Dislikes: *wimpy girls*

Favourite thing: *model aeroplane*

Worst habit: *telling on Kitty, being a goody two-shoes*

Most likely to say: *'Little sisters should respect their brothers!'*

Least likely to say: *'Kitty, you're the best.'* ← I am!

Favourite Kitty moment: *the surprise party she organised to make Daniel feel better about going to a new school.*

(And then there's Baby Tom, but he's only one and just says 'Ga-ga-ga-ga-ga!' all the time!)

he can also smile, crawl a bit, chew things and burp!

All about **You**

Name:

Favourite Kitty book:

Likes:

Dislikes:

Worst habit:

Most likely to say:

Least likely to say:

Favourite Kitty moment:

My family:

My pets:

I don't want
to clean my teeth!

Chapter 2

Kitty says ...

One thing that Kitty rarely does
is run out of words.
You might say that
Kitty has been known to raise
her voice. You could even say that
Kitty is REALLY QUITE LOUD!
And there are some phrases that
Kitty is certain to use at least
twice a day.

Here is Kitty's Top 10 ...

1.

I don't want to!

The first story ever told about Kitty was
all about the things she *didn't* want to do.
'I don't want to clean my teeth!'
'I don't want to eat my vegetables!'
'I don't want to go to bed!'

But sometimes it's not just that Kitty isn't in the
mood to do these things – it's that she doesn't
like being *told* what to do all the time!
(especially by the GUs!)

What things do you moan about doing?

I don't want to .... !

I don't want to .... !

I don't want to .... !

2. GUs

Who *always* thinks they're right? Who says 'We'll see', or 'Never mind' instead of answering your questions? Who keeps nagging you to tidy your room, clean your teeth and do your homework? It's the Grown-Ups! The GUs!

Kitty is always in trouble with one GU or another. And sometimes, the GUs are in trouble with her! But Kitty knows that being a GU is sometimes hard work – and some of them are quite nice!

Me being told off!

Who are your favourite GUs?

....

....

....

3.

I can't find it!

Kitty really doesn't like tidying her bedroom, and it's not just because Mum and Dad are always *telling* her to do it! She hates a tidy bedroom because it looks like nobody lives there – *they* like a tidy bedroom because Kitty's always losing things! In just one day Kitty lost:

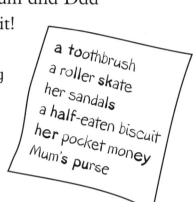

a toothbrush
a roller skate
her sandals
a half-eaten biscuit
her pocket money
Mum's purse

Dad told her she had to get more organised. So Kitty wrote a neat list of all the things she would need to take to school the next day. But the very next morning, Kitty said,

'I can't find my list!'

It turned up under my bed!

Are you always losing things too?

YES! I can't find _____ !

I can't find _____ !

I can't find _____ !

4.
It's not my fault!

Kitty is not exactly a 'morning person' – there's so much rushing around and organising to be done. Dan can never find his school things and then Dad gets cross and that makes Mum cross and then Baby Tom cries and Kitty whines and it's a mad house!

One morning (or rather, lots of mornings), Kitty was late for school, but she was determined that it was NOT HER FAULT! Do you know who she blamed when her teacher asked her why she was late? She blamed the clock for going too fast!

What makes you late for school?

....

....

....

5. I wish!

If Kitty had one wish,
she'd wish that every
wish she wished
would come true!
And then she'd
wish for lots of
chocolate, a new bike,
a big art set and roast
chicken every day.

One day Kitty wished for something quite
odd ... to be a GU! Kitty decided that GUs had
a much nicer time – they could watch TV when
they wanted, eat a biscuit when they felt like it
and go to bed only when they were *really tired*.
But Kitty only wished that for a very short time,
before she realised that being her own age
was MUCH MORE FUN!

If you had 3 wishes, what would you wish for?

I wish .... !

I wish .... !

I wish .... !

6. It's not fair!

Sometimes Kitty feels that things simply aren't fair – and it's especially unfair that her brother, Dan, is allowed to stay up later than she is! So Kitty moaned and she complained and she whined and she stomped about, until finally Mum agreed to do an experiment – Kitty could go to bed at the same time as her brother. Kitty was over the moon!

But as the days went by, lots of little things went wrong, and Kitty's head ached a bit, and she found herself longing to cuddle up to Mr Tubs. The final straw was when she slept through all of Saturday and missed a football game with Dad. From then on Kitty realised how lovely sleep really is!

What makes you say *'It's not fair!'*?

It's not fair   !

It's not fair   !

It's not fair   !

7.
But you promised!

Kitty gets really annoyed with people who break their promises. She thinks the worst culprits are GUs. They say one thing, but they

really mean another. Like when Kitty had to go to the doctor to have an injection, and she didn't want to go (she even hid under the table), and Dad PROMISED it wouldn't hurt. The doctor said the same thing. But it DID hurt. Dad was very sorry that the injection had hurt Kitty, and sorry that his promise had been broken, but he explained that sometimes when GUs say 'I promise' they really mean 'I hope'. And after all, GUs aren't in charge of everything!

But I didn't cry!

Write down one promise you have kept, and one promise you had to break.

A kept promise: ....

A broken promise: ....

8. I'm bored!

Sometimes when Kitty gets bored, it's like a curtain comes down inside her head and she can't think what to do – so she just gets more bored! And whenever she asks a GU to help her stop being bored, they always suggest boring things that you only want to do when you're not bored already! Does that make sense? Usually Kitty loves reading and painting and playing with her toys – but when she feels flat, even those things seem boring.

But when Kitty has a flash of inspiration, you'd better watch out – because nobody's going to be bored then!

What makes you feel bored?

....

....

....

9. Why not?

There are days when Kitty doesn't want to do the things that GUs want her to do, and there are days when she wants to do things and they won't let her! Then instead of saying 'I don't want to!' she says 'Why not?' Like when she wanted to walk to school on her own, or go trick-or-treating. There's one thing the GUs are guaranteed to say in reply – 'No, because I say so!' Sometimes Kitty manages to wriggle her way out of little problems like that! (And other times, she has to grit her teeth and admit that they were right to say no.)

What are you not allowed to do?

....

....

What reason did the GU give you?

....

....

10.
So what!

When Kitty feels like everyone is getting at her for no reason, her usual response is 'So what!' She likes to pretend that she doesn't care about things, just to stop the GUs from nagging. But one thing she couldn't pretend she didn't care about was when her best friend Mr Tubs got left behind in Spain after their summer holiday. Kitty was very brave and said that it didn't matter that he was left behind because she was too big for bears, but everyone knew how much she cared. Luckily Mr Tubs flew all the way home in a big brown parcel! She didn't say 'So what' to that!

What is your favourite toy?

I can't find
my roller skates!

Chapter 3

Kitty's Anti-Boredom Rules

Too much TV is BORING!

Sometimes, Kitty likes watching TV, like when there's a good programme on about nature, or something funny. But watching it all day is boring (and anyway, Daniel never lets her choose which channel to watch). Mum says that the most boring thing in the world is children saying things are boring. Here are Kitty's ideas for what to do instead.

RULE NUMBER 1:

with friends it's more fun!

THROW A RAIN PARTY!

You will need:
food for a picnic
a shed or a home-made tent
a tray
a tea towel
paper and pencils
a scarf
a few friends!

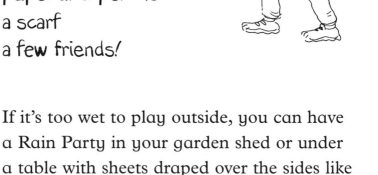

If it's too wet to play outside, you can have
a Rain Party in your garden shed or under
a table with sheets draped over the sides like
a tent. Make a picnic and invite a few friends.

These are Kitty's best Rain Party games ...

The Rain Party Word Game
(for 4 players)

Everyone needs a sheet of paper and a pencil. Write 16 words on little pieces of paper, fold them up and put them in a bowl. Everyone must choose 4 words. You have 10 minutes to write a short story using all the words. Then read them all out to each other – and you could get a GU to guess who wrote each story!

(For 5 players, write 20 words on the little pieces of paper; for 6 players write 24 words, and so on.)

Now give the best stories a title and write them in here so you can keep them forever.

What's that noise?
(for any number of players)

You will need a tape recorder for this game.
Secretly record lots of different sounds onto a
tape, using things you find around your house.
Then play the sounds to your friends and see
how many they can guess!

IDEAS FOR NOISES:
grinding pepper in a pepper mill
closing a creaking door

tapping a saucepan lightly with a whisk
stacking plates one after another
(but don't break them!)

rattling spoons in a drawer
shaking a box of cereal
flicking the pages of a book

blowing into the top of
an empty milk bottle

Heads, Bodies and Legs
(for 4 players)

Give everyone a sheet of paper and a pencil.
In secret, everyone draws a head on their sheet
of paper, then folds it over so that the fold
touches the very tip of their drawing, and passes
it to the person on their left. Now everyone
draws a body, down to the waist, and folds it
over again, and passes it to their left. Next draw
the hips and legs right down to the ankles; fold
it over and pass on. Finally, draw the feet or
shoes, fold it over and pass on. Now everyone
opens up their picture!

The Taste Test
(for any number of players)

Put little bits of food on a tray (about 10 different kinds) and cover with a tea towel. Now blindfold each player using a scarf. Make sure they don't peek! Put a little bit of food in their mouths and ask them to guess what it is. The person who guesses the most correctly is the winner. You can make it even more fun by using foods that feel like horrible things, like eyeballs, fingers and brain!

IDEAS FOR FOODS TO TRY:

peeled grapes ← (these feel like eyeballs!)
soggy crisps

tomato seeds
peeled orange segment
sliced strawberries
jelly
tinned carrots
frankfurters ← (these feel like fingers!)
(worms!) → spaghetti
leftover cold potatoes ← (brain!)

RULE NUMBER 2:

just me and you!

Kitty and William

Even great friends have tiffs – these two have tiffs over Snakes and Ladders, Snap, Chess, and especially water fights in the garden! But they enjoy working on things together, too.

Try these word games with a friend:

KITTY'S WORDSEARCH

Find these words in the grid, and circle them like the example shown:

~~Kitty~~, Baby Tom, Mr Tubs, bicycle, rollerskate, Christmas, football, Daniel, park, chocolate, school

S	B	R	E	K	A	P	S	W	E	K	C	A	V	V
T	I	W	N	I	D	T	I	F	S	I	E	F	E	A
A	C	Y	O	S	E	L	K	A	V	T	B	R	G	F
T	Y	I	R	T	L	Q	E	T	A	Z	R	F	G	U
E	C	A	M	I	D	H	L	K	O	E	S	O	Y	I
H	L	P	A	R	K	X	S	H	R	P	S	O	T	M
F	E	M	Q	A	Y	R	J	T	S	B	U	T	R	M
I	J	S	U	W	E	Z	F	U	Y	L	U	B	O	E
S	F	C	G	L	I	B	O	R	D	E	R	A	U	S
A	D	H	L	R	D	A	N	I	E	L	Q	L	B	W
S	E	O	B	I	O	B	D	G	B	Y	A	L	L	Q
C	R	O	V	K	E	Y	T	T	I	K	J	G	E	C
H	P	L	X	N	L	T	S	U	N	I	O	H	S	N
T	I	O	S	C	H	O	C	O	L	A	T	E	P	L
S	W	R	E	S	A	M	T	S	I	R	H	C	A	I

KITTY'S CLOCKWORD

The answers from 1 to 12 are all 5-letter words ending with the letter S. Write each one in the grid. The letters in the outer circle spell out one of Kitty's favourite meals.

1. The dog itching his fur might have _ _ _ _ S.

2. This book is full of BIG _ _ _ _ S to stop you being bored.

3. Plant some _ _ _ _ S in the garden.

4. At the back of your feet you have _ _ _ _ S.

5. Look up places in the world in a book called an _ _ _ _ S.

6. At the tips of your fingers and toes you have _ _ _ _ S.

7. If you are going to a party you might wear a _ _ _ _ S.

8. At the end of a good show the audience _ _ _ _ S.

9. On a golf course there are 18 _ _ _ _ S.

10. Dad _ _ _ _ S his shirt to get the creases out.

11. Turn over the _ _ _ _ S of a book to find out what happens.

12. In the night sky you will see thousands of _ _ _ _ S.

The yummy meal is: ....

35

Kitty and Anita

Anita is quite shy, but she has a very good imagination and she and Kitty make up great games. Their favourite is the 'If You Were' game. Kitty says: 'If you were an animal . . .' and Anita replies: 'I'd be a RABBIT, because I'm shy and I like company.' Then Anita says: 'If you were an animal . . .' and Kitty replies: 'I'd be a MONKEY, because I'm a bit wild and very energetic.' You can use any type of category for this game:

If you were . . .

a vegetable . . .
a bird . . .
a cartoon character . . .
a fruit . . .
a vehicle . . .

If you were...	ME	My Friend . . . .
...a vegetable		
...a bird		
...a cartoon character		
...a fruit		
...a vehicle		
...		
...		
...		
...		
...		
...		
...		

Kitty and Rosie

Rosie comes from a big family – three brothers and a sister! So her house is always noisy and she loves it when it's just her and Kitty.

Kitty and Rosie love to make each other laugh by doing strange things. Try some of these:

1. Do everything using your left hand (but use your right hand if you're left-handed!), like writing your name, drawing a picture or cleaning your teeth.

2. Do everything with your feet instead of your hands. Try picking up a pencil with your toes and then writing with it. Some people can even feed themselves using their feet!

3. Try saying everything backwards.
Instead of 'Hi, how are you, Rosie?'
say 'Rosie, you are how, hi?' Instead of,
'Kitty, you say the silliest things,' say
'Things silliest the say you, Kitty.'
It's harder than you think!

4. Paint each other's faces but try to hide
the colours you are using and don't tell
them what you are turning them into.
A witch? A monster? A beautiful butterfly?
Can they guess?

Give yourselves a mark out of 10 for each one.

	Me	My friend
Using other hand:	/10	/10
Using toes:	/10	/10
Backwards talking:	/10	/10
Face painting:	/10	/10

RULE NUMBER 3: only me!

Things to do on your own

Kitty loves being with her friends, but she likes
to spend some time on her own, too. She thinks
it's fun to be especially silly when she's alone
in her bedroom, and there's no one to say,
'Oh, Kit-kat!'

Kitty really makes herself laugh by turning
herself into a monster or a witch. Sit in front of
the mirror and draw your face. Then add some
monster or witch features and see if a picture of
your own face can scare you!

Some features you could add:

pointed eyebrows

hooked nose

flared nostrils

warts

wrinkles

scars

sharp teeth

messy hair

Draw your scary picture here.
Give yourself a scary name!

Kitty the Poet!

Once when Kitty was in her bedroom, wondering what to do, she wrote this:

Kitty's Rose Poem

There once was a girl called Rose,
Who had an enormous nose;
She had the worst habit,
Just like a little rabbit –
She picked and picked her nose!
She picked all night, she picked all day,
She picked it even during play,
Did Rose.
Her mum and dad said, 'Rose you're bad!'
They were ashamed! They felt so sad.
Her nose began to get a hole,
But still she dug just like a mole!
She cried, 'Why me?'
She was a sight to see,
But still she did not stop.
Her brother said, 'Oh you are dumb,
To pick your nose, not suck your thumb.'
Then one day she woke,
And before she spoke,
Her hand went to her nose.
But Rose got a shock,
For there was no nose . . .
So don't YOU be like disgusting Rose!

Write your own poem on this page. It doesn't have to be very long, it doesn't have to rhyme, and it doesn't even have to make sense. Just have fun!

It's not fair –
you always win!

Chapter 4

Daniel's bit

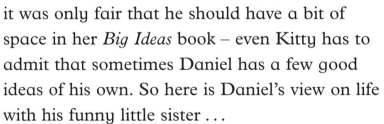

Even though Daniel can be a bit of a pain at times, Kitty thought it was only fair that he should have a bit of space in her *Big Ideas* book – even Kitty has to admit that sometimes Daniel has a few good ideas of his own. So here is Daniel's view on life with his funny little sister . . .

Oh, Kitty!

Being Kitty's big brother can be a real nuisance, but sometimes her silliness makes me laugh. These are my top 3 funniest Kitty moments:

1. Grotty Girl

After a day making mud pies in the garden, Kitty the grot-bag got into the bath with all her clothes on – she thought she could wash herself and her clothes at the same time!

2. Fuss-pot

When it comes to vegetables, Kitty would much rather have a biscuit or some chocolate. She was once so determined not to eat her vegetables (or as she calls them, veggy-troubles) that she went out into the garden and dug up all sorts of plants, then brought them back inside. She said she'd much rather eat her own veggy-troubles, so she asked Dad to cook the plants for her.

And she ate EVERY SINGLE BITE! We couldn't believe our eyes. Yuk! I bet there were worms in it.

What's your favourite food?

....

What's your least favourite food?

....

3. Princess Kitty

Kitty loves to look like a scruff-bag, but one day she got it into her head that she should look like our sissy cousin, Melissa. Imagine Kitty with neat hair in bunches and a party dress!

What's the funniest thing you've ever done?

....

....

....

....

....

....

Bibi v. Mr Tubs

The Big Contest!

Don't tell anyone, but of all my best things,
the squashed toy that Mum bought me in a
craft sale will always be my secret favourite.
Kitty thinks Mr Tubs is the best toy in the
world – but we'll see how Mr Tubs matches up
to Bibi . . .

Mr Tubs

Bibi

Name: Bibi	Name: Mr Tubs
Type of animal: cross between rabbit, koala bear and squirrel	Type of animal: bear
Looks: floppy and homemade	Looks: small, with a squashy nose, pink paws, sparkling eyes, fat tummy
Smells: of Dan's cuddles!	Smells: of Kitty's cuddles!
Lives: in a box in Dan's cupboard	Lives: on Kitty's bed
Job: to cheer Dan up when he's feeling fed up or scared	Job: Kitty's best friend
Score: 10 out of 10	Score: 10 out of 10

OK, fair enough – it's a tie!

Dan's perfect Saturday

School's not so bad, but nothing can beat a good Saturday – especially when you are allowed to do anything you like. This is what I'd do:

At 7 o'clock . . . I'd wake up and eat bacon, eggs, beans and toast

At 9 o'clock . . . I'd watch cartoons (I might let Kitty watch, too)

At 11 o'clock . . . I'd play football in the park (and score a goal)

At 1 o'clock . . . I'd eat chips and chocolate (as much as I like)

At 3 o'clock . . . I'd play computer games

At 5 o'clock . . . I'd play cricket (and score a century)

At 7 o'clock . . . I'd eat roast chicken and potatoes

At 9 o'clock . . . I'd watch a film (something scary)

At 11 o'clock . . . I'd tell ghost stories with my friends

And finally . . . I'd have a midnight feast!

don't tell Mum!

My perfect Saturday

At 7 o'clock...

....

At 9 o'clock...

....

At 11 o'clock...

....

At 1 o'clock...

....

At 3 o'clock...

....

At 5 o'clock...

....

At 7 o'clock...

....

At 9 o'clock...

....

At 11 o'clock...

....

And finally...

....

when Dan is a GU ...

I'm already quite grown-up, but when I'm as old as Dad I'll probably be a teacher, because I'm good at explaining things and I like children (well, most of them!). Either that or I'll be a famous cricketer. I think when Kitty grows up she'll be a writer, because she has so many funny things to say and she loves reading.

What will you be when you are a GU?

....

....

....

....

Baby Tom

It used to be just me, Mum, Dad and Kitty in our family – until along came a cute little baby we call Tom! I was really pleased when I found out I was getting a baby brother, so I could teach him things and play games and earn some money from baby-sitting, but you should have seen Kit-bag's face when she found out. She was scared that she'd stop being Mum's little girl – but as long as she acts like a baby there's no danger of that! She's a bit more used to him now.

We all fuss around Tom and he's really cool (except sometimes). Mum and Dad put on these silly voices when they talk to him, and Kitty and I copy them for fun. 'Hellosie wosie Tommy Wommy. Who's a cutsie wootsie boysie den?' Having a baby around is great, and it'll be even more great when he's old enough to play cricket and football!

But you promised
I could have a pet!

Chapter 5

William, Anita and Rosie's bit

Kitty wouldn't swap her friends for all the chocolate and roast chicken in the world! They make her laugh, they always listen when she has a problem, and they're all so different that Kitty can never get bored when she's with them. And best of all, they love Kitty just the way she is.

William

William and Kitty are so close that Kitty's mum calls them an old married couple (and that's because they argue, too, but always make up in the end).

What Kitty likes most about William:

Loyal
Kind to animals
Good at water fights
Lives next door!

(especially his
new cat, Cleo)

What William likes most about Kitty:

Not too girly
Likes the same things
Never boring
Good at chess

(William's big sister
taught me)

Anita

When Anita first
came to Kitty's
school, Kitty wasn't
sure that Anita
liked her, but they
soon cleared up the misunderstanding and
now they are firm friends.

What Kitty likes most about Anita:

Not too loud ←
Very pretty (not like me!)
Always thinks of others
Laughs at my jokes

What Anita likes most about Kitty:

Very brave
Makes people laugh
Good at organising
A bit naughty ←

(Who me?!)

Rosie

Kitty is very proud
of her friend Rosie
because she's good at so
many things – she's clever in
lessons as well as good at games. And
Kitty could never feel jealous about that
because having a good friend is the most
important thing.

What Kitty likes most about Rosie:

A bit mad like me!
Brainy
Tall ←—(can reach things!)
Very good at sport

What Rosie likes most about Kitty:

Chatty
Not like anyone else
Always laughing ←
Good at art

(ha! ha! ha!
ha! ha! ha!)

My Friends

Draw pic or
stick photo

Name:

Age:

Where we met:

What I like most about them:

What they like most about me:

Autograph:

```
┌─────────────────┐
│  Draw pic or    │
│  stick photo    │
└─────────────────┘
```

Name: ....

Age: ....

Where we met: ....

....

....

....

What I like most about them:

....

....

....

What they like most about me:

....

....

....

Autograph: ....

Draw pic or
stick photo

Name: ....

Age: ....

Where we met: ....

....

....

....

What I like most about them: ....

....

....

....

What they like most about me: ....

....

....

....

Autograph: ....

Draw pic or
stick photo

Name:

Age:

Where we met:

What I like most about them:

What they like most about me:

Autograph:

Draw pic or
stick photo

Name:

Age:

Where we met:

What I like most about them:

What they like most about me:

Autograph:

Draw pic or
stick photo

Name:

Age:

Where we met:

What I like most about them:

What they like most about me:

Autograph:

Draw pic or
stick photo

Name:

Age:

Where we met:

What I like most about them:

What they like most about me:

Autograph:

The Kitty Song

by William, Rosie and Anita

Kitty looks a real disgrace,
Jam and mud smeared on her face,
Won't have a bath,
Or wash her hair,
She simply roars out –
I DON'T CARE!

Kitty is a monster child,
Loud and angry, fierce and wild.
Won't clean her teeth,
So they'll all rot,
But she just yells out –
OH, SO WHAT!

Kitty's room is filled with mould,
She just won't do as she is told,
Won't tidy up,
Won't eat her tea,
She stamps and bellows –
NO! WHY ME?

But one girl is our number one,
She finds the best ways to have fun,
She makes us laugh,
She's smart and witty –
Who's our best friend?
Yes, it's KITTY!!

I wish
it was mine!

Chapter 6

Other bits 'n' bobs

Kitty got a real shock when she went into school one morning and saw how much her cousin had changed. If you knew the New Mel, you'd hardly believe she could ever have been the Old Melissa. New Mel is really cool to hang out with, but Old Melissa, well – see for yourself...

Old Melissa

Boring

Droopy curls

Show-off

Fussy

Only likes girls

Thinks everything is 'stupid'

Posh clothes

Unfriendly

Doesn't eat CHOCOLATE!!!

New Mel

Cheerful

NOT stuck-up

Friendly

Cares about friends

Generous

Comfortable clothes

(good for messing about in)

NICE!

So Melissa was a nice girl underneath – and do you know that all it took was a clever letter from Mr Tubs to bring the niceness out? (You can read the letter in *It's Not My Fault!*)

Kitty's wish list

Sometimes you have to be careful what you wish for, because you might discover that even if you think you really want something, what you've got already turns out to be better! These are Kitty's wishes, and her reasons why she might have to un-wish them.

I wish it was **always** Christmas . . .
(but then I'd miss out on summer, and I wouldn't have Christmas to look forward to, and I'd have to buy so many presents!)

I **wish** I was **grown-up** . . .
(but then I'd have to deal with tricky things and I'd have less time to play and I wouldn't be able to be silly!)

I wish **good** days would never end . . .
(but then I wouldn't be able to lie in bed thinking about the good days until finally falling asleep and dreaming about new good days!)

Sorting out what to wish for can be hard work!

My wish list

....

....

....

....

....

....

....

....

....

....

....

....

How to handle GUs

Without a doubt, Kitty's favourite GUs in the world are her mum and dad. They might nag her to tidy her room, and tell her to eat all her veggy-troubles, but Kitty loves them more than anything. And when it comes to getting round their funny little ways, Kitty has learnt a thing or two.

1. Wear their shoes!

I don't mean their *real* shoes, but it's good to understand what it's like to be a **GU** *sometimes*. Once when Mum was really fed up I told her to go upstairs and lie on her bed with one of those funny mud masks on her face, while I rushed around doing lots of little jobs for her. I was Mummy Kitty!

2. Make them laugh

Mum already says I'm the funniest girl in the world (she sometimes says I'm also the naughtiest but never mind about that!). If you make a GU smile once in a while, they might remember not to be so serious all the time.

3. Gobbledygook

GUs use all sorts of long words, and the way they find them is by reading and reading and putting lots of words into their brains, sort of like saving pocket money. If you ever hear a GU struggling to find the right word, perhaps you can pop one into their sentence for them - a really good long one!

4. Surprise, surprise!

Sometimes GUs think about work too much and forget to have fun. Once Dad even forgot their wedding anniversary, when he'd promised to take Mum out! So me and Dan set up a table in the garden, with flowers on the table and candles and music. They thought it was really romantic.

5. Hush, hush!

When Mum, Dad and Dan moaned about how much I teased them and joked around, I decided to turn all polite and quiet to see if they'd prefer me that way. In only a little while they were begging me to turn back into my old self - so of course I did!

Kitty's Whys

Sometimes Kitty has a bit of an outburst and gets all of her 'why' questions out in one go. Can you help her fill in the answers to these whys?

Why are GUs allowed to interrupt children, if children aren't allowed to interrupt GUs?

....

Why do people dig up woods and fields just to build offices?

....

Why do people bully other people?

....

Why can't we just stay as we are?

....

Sleep tight

Kitty loves reading stories, and she loves
writing them, too. The best stories can come
from your own dreams,
so write down a dream
each morning and
see if you
can make
a good
story out
of them.

I'm scared of
the dark!

Chapter 7

The best bits
of my year

Kitty loves to have little reminders of what she's
done all year – she does so much she might
forget some of it if she didn't
write it down once in a
while! Here's a place for
you to write some of your
best memories of each
month of the year.

JANUARY

Best book

Best day out

Best day in

Best meal

Best TV programme

FEBRUARY

Best book

Best day out

Best day in

Best meal

Best TV programme

MARCH

Best book

Best day out

Best day in

Best meal

Best TV programme

APRIL

Best book

Best day out

Best day in

Best meal

Best TV programme

Best book

Best day out

Best day in

Best meal

Best TV programme

JUNE

Best book

Best day out

Best day in

Best meal

Best TV programme

JULY

Best book

Best day out

Best day in

Best meal

Best TV programme

AUGUST

Best book

Best day out

Best day in

Best meal

Best TV programme

SEPTEMBER

Best book

Best day out

Best day in

Best meal

Best TV programme

OCTOBER

Best book

Best day out

Best day in

Best meal

Best TV programme

NOVEMBER

Best book

Best day out

Best day in

Best meal

Best TV programme

DECEMBER

Best book

Best day out

Best day in

Best meal

Best TV programme

I know I'm
right!

Chapter 8

Kitty's Big Quiz

Are you naughty like Kitty, clever like Daniel, snooty like Melissa or easygoing like William? Find out in this brilliant quiz . . . no cheating!

Tick the closest answer in these 14 questions, add up your score and check the results!

1. What is your favourite colour?

a. Red
b. Blue
c. Pink
d. Green

2. What is your most prized possession?

a. Bicycle
b. Party dress
c. Cricket bat
d. Teddy bear

3. What would you say if you were losing a game of Snakes and Ladders?

a. Let's play dressing-up instead.
b. You're cheating!
c. It's not fair - you always win!
d. Huh, I'll win the next game.

4. What makes you feel most scared?

a. The dark (but only sometimes)
b. Ghosts - wooooh!
c. Big changes, like going to a new school
d. Acting on stage in front of lots of people

5. If you had one wish, what would you wish for?

a. Lots of chocolate and a new bike
b. That every wish I wished would come true
c. To be a bit bigger and stronger
d. A big party with lots of presents all for me!

6. What makes you feel bored?

a. Boys
b. Too much homework
c. People ignoring me
d. Girly stuff like dolls and make-up

7. What would you say if you were late for school?

a. It's not my fault –
   it was everyone else!
b. It took me ages to do my hair.
c. Sorry! I was buried in a brilliant book.
d. I'm never late for school.

8. If you could have any pet you wanted, what would you choose?

a. Hamster
b. Cat
c. Dog
d. I don't really like animals.

9. How naughty are you?

a. I'm naughty . . . but nice!
b. Not naughty at all.
c. Only sometimes, depending on who I'm with.
d. Well, I'm good when I want something.

10. What makes you most cross?

a. Mess
b. Bullies and goody-goodies
c. People who make a nuisance of themselves
d. I hardly ever get cross

11. On a Saturday afternoon, what do you most like to do?

a. Go for an adventure in the woods
b. Play football in the park
c. Do some gardening
d. Have a dolls'
   tea party

12. Which of these naughty things do you do the most?

a. Eat sweets after I've cleaned my teeth.
b. Refuse to share toys with my friends.
c. Complain when I'm asked to do
   something.
d. Boast about winning games.

13. Which of these is it most important to be?

a. Clever
b. Pretty
c. Funny
d. Kind

14. What's your idea of a great holiday?

a. An adventure holiday
b. Somewhere warm by the sea, with lots to do
c. A pretty cottage in the quiet countryside, with roses round the door
d. A boat trip

How to score:

1. a5, b3, c2, d4 □
2. a4, b2, c3, d5 □
3. a2, b3, c5, d4 □
4. a5, b2, c3, d4 □
5. a5, b3, c4, d2 □
6. a2, b3, c5, d4 □
7. a5, b2, c4, d3 □
8. a5, b4, c3, d2 □
9. a5, b2, c4, d3 □
10. a2, b5, c4, d3 □
11. a5, b4, c3, d2 □
12. a5, b2, c3, d4 □
13. a3, b2, c5, d4 □
14. a4, b5, c2, d3 □

Now put your total
in this box ⟶ □

The Results!

61-80
You are most like ...

Kitty!

You talk like her, dress like her, and you're definitely as naughty as her! The great thing about you is that no matter how mischievous you are, people can't help forgiving you because of your great sense of humour and your warm heart.

41-60
You are most like ...

William!

Like Kitty, you know how to have fun, and you like your friends to be the same.

You are kind and easygoing, but you sometimes like to have your own way, too! You like being out and about, and you're a good friend.

21-40
You are most like...

(Daniel!)

You are smart and quite grown-up,
sometimes too grown-up!
You don't like being too silly
and sometimes silly people annoy
you, but you have a fun streak too
and you are very good company.

0-20
You are most like...

(Melissa!)

You like the pretty, peaceful things
in life, and turn your nose up at
rough games and loud people. You
can be a bit snooty, but underneath,
you're sweet and kind – it's just a question of
how to get it out!

And that is the end of my book of Big Ideas.

I hope you had fun. If you have any Big Ideas of your own, or if you have any questions for me or Bel, you can visit Bel's website at **www.bel-mooney.co.uk** and leave us a message.

Bye everyone!